W9-AXT-376

This igloo book belongs to:

_____

igloobooks

Published in 2016
by Igloo Books Ltd
Cottage Farm
Sywell
NN6 0BJ
www.igloobooks.com

Original story by Igloo Books Ltd
Party Paws™ & A Little Bear Called Bamboo™
are registered Trade Marks of © Artworld Inspirations Limited

All rights reserved. No part of this publication may be reproduced,
stored in a retrieval system, or transmitted in any way or by any means, electronic,
mechanical, photocopying, recording or otherwise, without the prior written
permission of the publisher.

REX001 0816
6 8 10 9 7
ISBN: 978-0-85780-850-9

Printed and manufactured in China

Daddy and Me

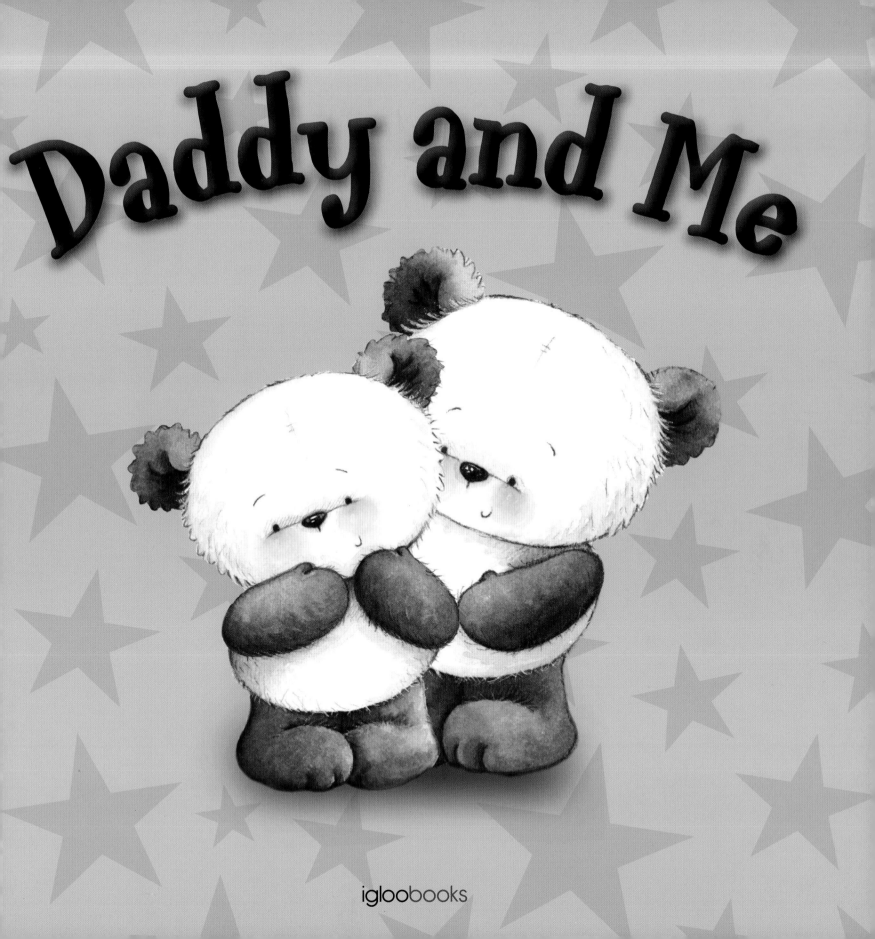

igloobooks

I love my daddy because he is big and strong and we do lots of fun things together.

Daddy makes me laugh and giggle.
I like to do silly dances, just like him.

Daddy and me love to be outside.
We play lots and lots of ball games together.

I love playing hide-and-seek. I'm brilliant at hiding and it takes Daddy ages to find me.

In the afternoon, I have a nap.
Daddy snuggles me into my special bed.

When the night-time comes,
we sit and look up at the twinkling stars.

I love helping Daddy in the garden.
I've got my own wheelbarrow and tools.

My daddy says it is really important
to take care of the pretty butterflies.

When it's sunny, Daddy takes me to the lake and I play with my blue sailing boat.

Daddy's big red car goes vroom-vroom.
Sometimes he takes me for a ride.

Daddy is really clever and he says if I read
lots of books I will be clever, too.

For Daddy's birthday, I make him a card.
It says, "Happy Birthday, Daddy."

Daddy and me love to paint together,
but Mummy says we make a terrible mess.

Daddy is really good at building things and
I love it when he lets me help.

My daddy makes my birthday really special.
We play party games and I open my presents.

Daddy bakes me a yummy birthday cake.
The best bit is eating the cherry on the top.

I love swimming in the sea with Daddy.
All day long, we splish and splash about.

Daddy and me watch the sun go down.
We snuggle up and have a lovely cuddle.

My daddy gives me soft, warm hugs.
He always makes me feel safe.

At bedtime, Daddy tucks me in and
gives me a big kiss goodnight.

My daddy is the best in the whole world and that's why I love him!

Best Daddy in the World